811119 '10|1

APR 7 1988

Childrens Press International
Distributed by Childrens Press, Chicago.
1987 School and Library Edition

Library of Congress Cataloging-in-Publication Data

Mahy, Margaret.
  A pet to the vet.

  Summary: As the neighbors wait in the veterinarian's
waiting room with their sick pets, a chain of events
begins which cures almost everyone.
  [1. Pets—Fiction.] I. Webb, Philip, ill. II. Title.
PZ7.M2773Pe   1987   [E]   87-854
ISBN 0-516-08978-1

Created and Designed by Wendy Pye, Ltd.

A Pet to the Vet

CHILDRENS PRESS INTERNATIONAL

Judy was very fond of her pet mouse Max.
He could dance and sing.
Not many mice can do this
but Max was a very clever mouse.

One morning,
Judy heard a teeny, tiny sneeze.
How terrible!
Max had a cold in his head.

"Oh dear," said Judy.
"A mouse with a wheeze
and a cough and a sneeze.
I'm taking my pet to the vet.
A pet to the vet,
A pet to the vet,
A pet to the vet, in the morning."

3

Next door,
Johnny went out to give
his rough, tough tomcat Tom some milk.
But Tom was limping and one of his ears
was all tattered around the edge.

"Oh dear," said Johnny.
"I can tell your paw
is terribly sore.
I'm taking my pet to the vet.
A pet to the vet,
A pet to the vet,
A pet to the vet, in the morning."

4

Halfway down the road,
Mrs. Black said, "Good morning,"
to her polly parrot.
The polly parrot was bored.
She yawned and scratched her ear
and not a word would she say.

"Oh dear," said Mrs. Black.
"A parrot so quiet
needs a change in its diet.
I'm taking my pet to the vet.
A pet to the vet,
A pet to the vet,
A pet to the vet, in the morning."

Near the end of the road,
Mr. Simpson went out to give
his pet snake Sampson
an egg beaten up in milk.
But during the night
Sampson had tossed and turned so much
he had tied himself in a big knot.

"Oh dear," cried Mr. Sampson.
"A knot in my snake!
What a dreadful mistake!
I'm taking my pet to the vet.
A pet to the vet,
A pet to the vet,
A pet to the vet, in the morning."

In the second to last house,
Sir Leopold tried to read jokes
to his laughing hyena.
But the hyena looked very sad
and would not laugh.

"Oh dear," said Sir Leopold.
"A hyena that's sad,
it looks very bad.
I'm taking my pet to the vet.
A pet to the vet,
A pet to the vet,
A pet to the vet, in the morning."

10

11

At the very end of the road
was the vet's house.
He had a very big letter box
with his name and all his initials on it.

This was his name:
Andrew Nicholas Icharus Malcolm
Archibald Lorenzo Lover.

A.N.I.M.A.L. Lover.

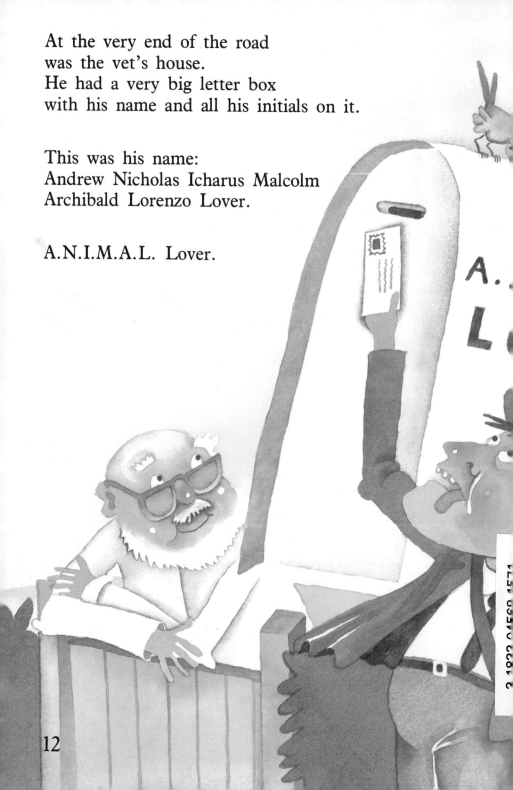

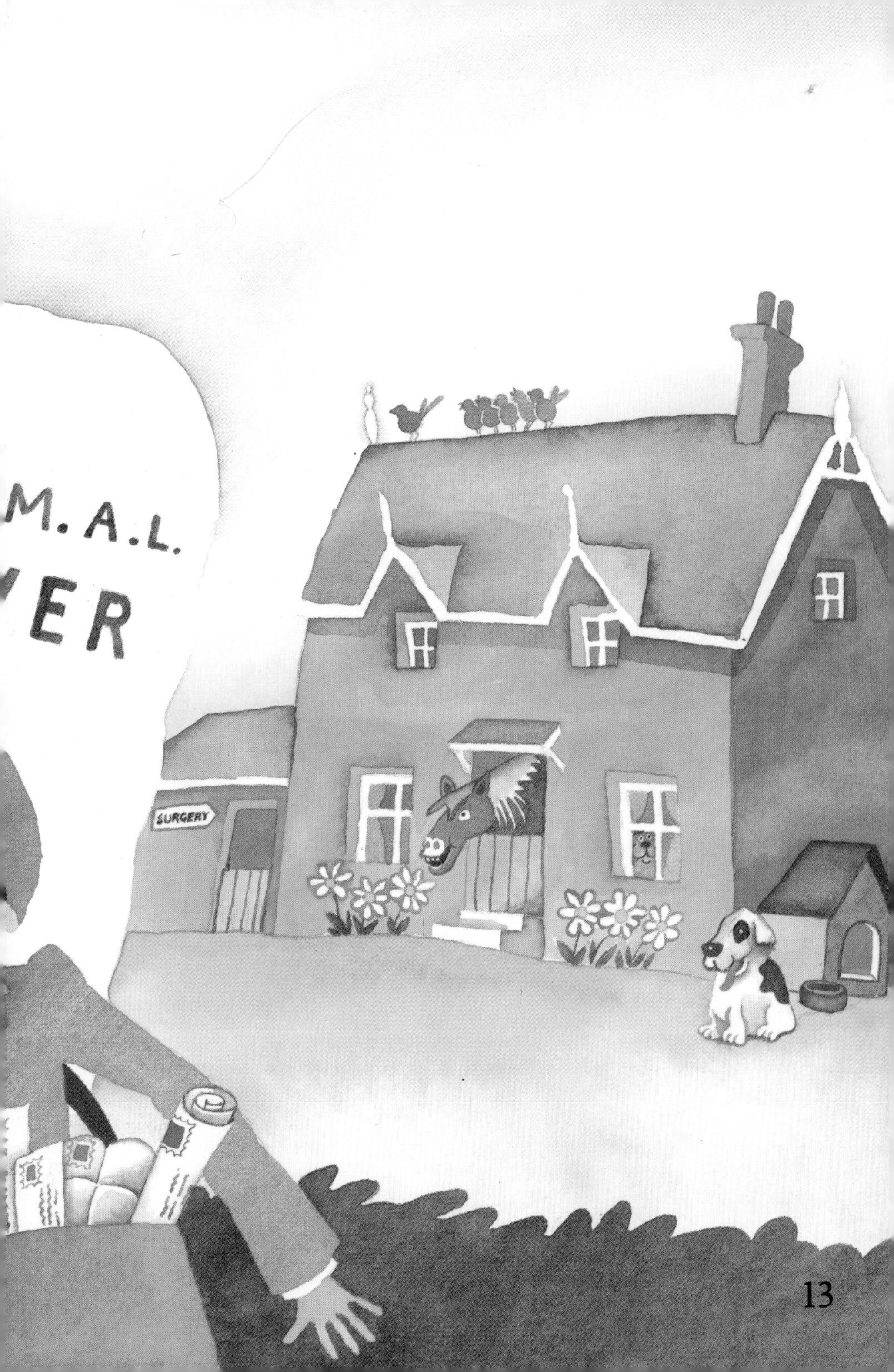
M.A.L.
VER
SURGERY

In the vet's waiting room
Judy sat with her pet mouse Max.

Johnny had his pet cat Tom.

Mrs. Black sat with her polly parrot.

Mr. Simpson sat with his snake Sampson.

Sir Leopold had his sad hyena.

15

Tom the cat saw Max the mouse.

"Breakfast!" thought Tom
and his tail began to twitch.

Sampson the snake saw the twitching tail.
"Really!" thought Sampson.
"A snake with fur!"

"How are you, brother?" he hissed.

He hissed so hard that the knot in his middle began to
untie itself.

17

Tom the cat sprang at Max the mouse.
Max leaped out of Judy's hands
and ran to the top of a potted plant.

"How do you do, my dear little brother?"
hissed Sampson to Tom's tail.

Tom turned around. He saw Sampson.

"It's a worm!" Tom cried.
"A great big cat-eating worm!"

He sprang into the plant too.

18

The polly parrot was so surprised
at what she saw
that she began to talk again.
She said,
"Cat after mouse
and snake after cat.
What will the vet
have to say about that?"

Sir Leopold's sad hyena
burst into a loud laugh.
Haw, haw, haw, haw!

The loud laugh frightened Sampson so much
that he straightened himself out instantly.
You would never have guessed
there had been a big knot in him.

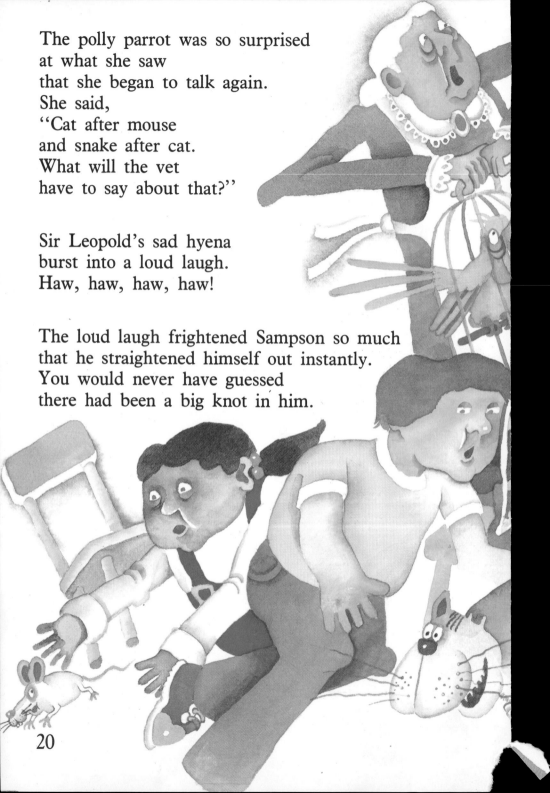

The door opened.
Out came Mr. Andrew Nicholas Icharus Malcolm
Archibald Lorenzo Lover the vet.

"My hyena's laughing again,"
said Sir Leopold. "I'll take him home."

"Sampson's untied himself,"
said Mr. Simpson. "I'll take him home."

"My polly parrot's talking again,"
said Mrs. Black. "I'll take her home."

"Tom has stopped limping,"
said Johnny. "I'll take him home."

Only Max the mouse was left.

Mr. A.N.I.M.A.L. Lover gave him
some special mouse medicine.
"He must have plenty of cheese," he said.
"And a lemon drink with honey in it."

23

Judy took Max home again.

Soon he was as well as ever.
He began to dance again,
and as he danced,
this is what he sang:
"A pet to the vet,
A pet to the vet,
A pet to the vet, in the morning."